Teaching and Learning
Key Stage 2
Differentiated Activity Book

Letts
EDUCATIONAL

Word

Literacy

Year 5

Contents

Introduction

Differentiated Activity Books:

- support the teaching of the Literacy Hour
- help meet the majority of the objectives of the National Literacy Strategy Framework
- contain 30 units of work, sufficient for one school year
- are straightforward and easy to use
- have a clear teaching focus
- contain differentiated activities for each objective at foundation, intermediate and challenging levels of difficulty.

Features of the Word Level Teaching Units

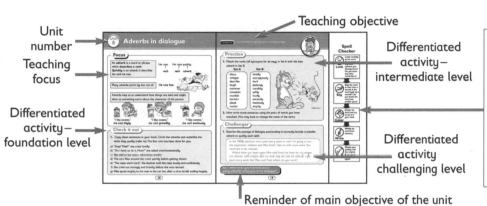

Unit number

Teaching focus

Differentiated activity – foundation level

Teaching objective

Differentiated activity – intermediate level

Differentiated activity challenging level

The fold out ready reference flap (inside back cover) provides children with a reminder of a consistently useful spelling strategy which can always be applied when teaching new words

Reminder of main objective of the unit

Using the Differentiated Activity Books

A Variety of Uses

The books may be used to:

- introduce and teach individual National Literacy Strategy Framework objectives independently
- introduce individual National Literacy Strategy Framework objectives prior to studying them during Text Level work
- consolidate, develop and extend National Literacy Strategy Framework objectives studied during Text Level work
- provide work for whole class, group or individual work
- provide work for follow-up homework assignments.

Class Work

The Teaching focus provides a clear explanation of each objective with examples for discussion. Appropriate activities may be chosen from the range of differentiated tasks for discussion, or to work through, with the class.

Group and Individual Work

The Differentiated Activity Books are ideal for group and individual work. Work on the same objective may be realistically matched appropriately to individual children's abilities, allowing children to work independently.

Homework

The material in the books provides an ideal solution to meaningful homework assignments that can be differentiated appropriately for each pupil.

Focus

A **prefix** is a group of letters that is added to the **beginning** of a word to change its meaning.

happy can become **un**happy

way can become **sub**way

Pre comes from Latin and means **before**.
So a **prefix** is something that you 'fix' before the word.

Prefixes often come from Greek or Latin and can mean something quite specific.

pre + fix = **prefix**

Check it out

1. Write out the words below and underline the prefixes in each one. The first one has been started for you.

   a) <u>un</u>happy, unlike, unclear
   b) inside, inborn, incredible
   c) surface, surname, surplus
   d) prefix, prehistoric, precaution
   e) exclaim, exit, extinguish
   f) centipede, centurion, centimetre
   g) dislike, disappear, disapprove

2. Look carefully at the meanings of each prefix you have underlined. Write what each prefix might mean, for example, a centipede has a hundred legs, so **cent** could mean **one hundred**.

Practice

1. Complete the sentences in Box A by choosing a prefix from the Prefix Box to make a new word.

Box A

Another name for a car is an _____.

The distance all around a circle is the _____.

The story of someone's life written by someone else is a _____.

A boat which sails under water is a _____.

Three children born at the same birth are called _____.

Across the Atlantic Ocean is called _____.

To choose wrongly is to make a _____.

A device for reproducing sounds and for talking over a distance is called a _____.

Prefix Box

auto

bi

trans

tele

circum

tri

sub

mis

2. Find some more examples of words which use each of the prefixes in the prefix box. Explain what they mean.

Challenger

1. Copy and complete the table. Use a dictionary to help.

Prefix	Meaning	Two examples
octo/a		octopus octagon
semi		
mono		
anti		
quad		
re		
inter		
super		

So – what have you learned about prefixes and how can they help you spell?

Unit 2 Suffixes

Focus

A **suffix** is a group of letters which is added to the end of a word to change its meaning.

Soft can become **softness** or **soften**.

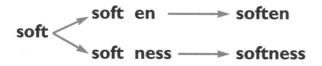

soft → soft en → soften

soft ness → softness

Sometimes you can recognise ancient Greek or Latin suffixes which have specific meanings.

The suffix **graph** or **graphy** comes from an ancient Greek word meaning **to write about.** So **geo-graphy** is the study of (writings about) the earth (geo).

Check it out

1. Write out the words below and underline the suffix in each example. The first one has been started for you.

a) advertise<u>ment</u>, encouragement, movement

b) washable, breakable, movable

c) accidental, musical, national

d) dirty, watery, angry

e) childish, foolish, girlish

f) girlhood, boyhood, childhood

g) shopping, hoping, crashing

2. Write the root words to which the suffix has been added.

Practice

1. Add suffixes from the Suffix Box to the words in List A to make as many new
words as you can. Do it like this: **hop – hopped – hopping**

List A

hop	shop	big	plan	swim	skip
fun	rub	clap	win	lean	pat
wag	wet	fat	thin	cook	pin
	skin	chop	chat	blot	

Suffix Box

en	ish	ed
ing	et	er
able	est	y

2. Underline the words you have made which double their last consonant
when you add a suffix. Write a rule for these words.

Challenger

1. **arian** is a Latin suffix which means **the grouping of people**. Choose a word
in the box to match each meaning below. Write your answers in your book.
Use a dictionary to help.

| librarian | vegetarian | utilitarian | discipinarian | valetudinarian |

a) Something designed to be useful.

b) Someone who doesn't eat meat.

c) A person who works in a library.

d) A person who believes in
good behaviour.

e) Someone with ill-health.

2. **ology** is a Greek suffix. Copy and complete
the puzzle making three more **ology** words.
Find out what the suffix means.

psych	ology
	ology
	ology
	ology

So – what have you learned about suffixes
and how they can help you to spell?

Focus

A **word root** is a word to which a prefix and a suffix can be added to make a different word.

Clear is a word all by itself.

It is the root of **unclear** and **clearly**.

clear   **un**clear   clear**ly**

↑   ↑
prefix   suffix

Check it out

1. Write out the words below and underline the word roots in each example. The first one has been started for you.

a) <u>help</u>ing, unhelpful, helpless

b) football, footpath, footstool

c) childhood, childish, children

d) invent, prevent, advent

e) impart, apart, departure

f) pressure, pressing, depress

g) microphone, telephone, phonics

h) signal, signature, signed

2. Beside each word, write whether a prefix or a suffix has been used to change the word root.

Practice

1. Make some new words by adding a suffix to the end of the word root or a prefix to the beginning. Choose from the words in the boxes below.

Do it like this: **ordinary – extraordinary** or **copy – copying**

Prefixes

dis	extra
sub	micro
photo	super
anti	

Word roots

ordinary	terrestrial	scope
copy	marine	approve
appear	way	graph
wave	market	social

Suffixes

ing	ed
ic	ing
al	

Use a dictionary to check your words.

2. Write each word in a sentence to show that you know what they mean.

Challenger

1. Many word roots come from ancient languages, such as Latin, and are not whole words, for example:

dico, dictus (I say, said)   **scribo, scriptus** (I write, written)
voco, vocatus (I call, called)   **audio, suditus** (I hear, heard)
pes, pedis (the foot, of the foot) **sonus** (a sound)
terra (earth)   **novus, nova** (new)

Find some words which use these ancient word roots and complete the table.

Ancient word root	Meaning	Examples
dico, dictus	I say, said	dictophone, dictionary

So – what have you learned about word roots and how they can help you to spell?

Focus

Plural means **more than one**. When we change something from singular (one only) to plural, the spelling often changes.

The most common way of forming the plural of a noun is to add an **s**.

When you form the plural of most nouns ending in **ch**, **sh**, **ss** and **x**, you add **es**.

One green bottle standing on the wall.
Ten green bottle**s** standing on the wall.

At the jumble sale, I bought two brush**es** in box**es**, some match**es** and three wine glass**es**.

Check it out

1. Copy the sentences below. Circle each noun if it is singular and underline it if it is plural. Do it like this: **My mum goes to the shop every day** becomes **My (mum) goes to the <u>shops</u> every (day)**

a) Mum buys vegetables and sweets for me.

b) My friends were sitting on the benches in the park.

c) They were talking about seeing foxes in the bushes by the church last night.

d) All the church-goers in the area have been told to look out for thrushes and other wild birds.

e) The boys and girls were miserable.

f) They had lost their bus passes.

g) They will not be allowed on the buses any more.

2. Explain how you know that the underlined nouns are plurals.

Practice

1. Write out and complete these plural sums:

a) one bush + one bush = two _____

b) one lunch + one lunch = two _____

c) one smash + one smash = two _____

d) one fox + one fox = two _____

e) one grass + one grass = two _____

f) one watch + one watch = two _____

g) one glass + one glass = two _____

h) one rash + one rash = two _____

i) one ranch + one ranch = two _____

Check your answers in a dictionary.

Challenger

1. Copy and complete this table. Find five more nouns for each column.

Word endings			
s	**ch**	**sh**	**x**
bus			ox

2. Write some sentences using each word, first in the singular and then in the plural. Check your plurals in a dictionary.

Be careful – some plurals may not follow these rules!

So – what have you learned about spelling words when you make them plural?

Spelling plurals 2

Focus

Plural means **more than one**. When we change something from singular (one only) to plural, the spelling often changes.

When you form the plural of most nouns ending in **f** or **fe**, the **f** or **fe** changes to **ves**.

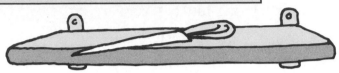

There is a knife on the shelf.
There are two kni**ves** on the shel**ves.**

When you form the plural of most nouns ending in **y**, two rules apply.

If a consonant comes before the **y**, it changes to **ies**.

one lady becomes **two ladies.**

If a vowel comes before the **y**, just add **s**.

one monkey becomes **two monkeys.**

Check it out

1. Write the plural form of each word.

a) one thief, two _____

b) one party, two _____

c) one city, two _____

d) one poppy, two _____

e) one penny, two _____

f) one jockey, two _____

g) one shelf, two _____

2. Write the singular form of each word.

a) two wives, one _____

b) two rubies, one _____

c) two monkeys, one _____

d) two ponies, one _____

e) two butterflies, one _____

f) two daisies, one _____

g) two wolves, one _____

Practice

1. Choose appropriate words from the box to complete each sentence. Copy the sentences, using your chosen words in the plural.

a) The farmers sold two ____ as well as other farm animals.

b) Our two ____ have shared their holidays for the past two years.

c) They cut the two ____ into two ____.

d) The beautiful ____ were put into vases and placed on opposite ____.

e) We walked through two beautiful steep-sided ____.

f) The exiles never forgot their three ____.

2. Write plural sentences of your own using the five remaining words.

> calf
> baby
> family
> valley
> country
> loaf
> lily
> shelf
> wolf
> thief
> half
> gypsy
> charity

Challenger

1. Write the singular words in the boxes in your book. Then write the correct rule for making them plural beside each word.

| donkey | holiday | sky | knife | journey | fairy | self |

Rule: change last two letters to **ves**.

Rule: vowel before final letter – add **s**.

Rule: change final consonant to **ves**.

Rule: no vowel before final letter – change last letter to **ies**.

b) Write out the plurals of each singular word.

2. Find the plurals of these words in your dictionary:

| cliff | dwarf | roof | scarf | wharf | hoof |

So – what have you learned about using punctuation effectively for meaning?

Focus

Synonyms are words with the **same meaning**, or very **similar meanings**. So **hot** can mean the same as: **boiling, fiery, scorching, sizzling**.

Choosing the right **synonym** for the particular situation is most important.

Your cup of tea could be boiling, not fiery.

A summer's day will be scorching or sizzling, not fiery.

A curry can be fiery, not scorching.

Check it out

1. Copy these examples in your book. Underline the synonym of the first word. The first one has been done for you.

a) hot   =   <u>boiling</u>, cold, hard, soft

b) say   =   voice, speak, see, whistle

c) get   =   go, come, catch, fetch

d) find   =   discover, lose, read, put

e) like   =   hate, enjoy, dislike, boast

f) think =   believe, brain, speak, muddle

g) see   =   hear, view, dark, look

h) hit   =   fall, strike, yelp, creep

Look up the words in a dictionary if you are unsure of their meaning.

2. Find one more synonym for each starter word.

Practice

1. Copy and complete the sentences below. Choose the most appropriate verbs for **to walk** from the Synonym Box. You may need to use them in the past tense.

Synonym Box

march	stroll
stride	shuffle
creep	pace
plod	saunter
strut	trudge

a) The sick man _____ slowly through the hospital ward on his crutches.

b) The miners _____ home after their tiring day underground.

c) The band _____ proudly through the town.

d) Jo _____ back into the house so she would not wake her parents.

e) All the holidaymakers _____ through the park on the sunny day.

f) The worried mother _____ the hospital corridor near her sick child.

g) Because they were not worried by the teacher, they _____ casually back into the lesson.

2. Write new sentences of your own using the three synonyms which remain.

Challenger

1. Write the ten synonyms for **cold** that you can find in the word search.

2. Write them in what you think is the right order, starting with the coldest and moving towards the least cold.

a	r	c	t	i	c	a	p	g
c	o	o	l	b	h	o	h	b
f	r	e	e	z	i	n	g	l
r	q	l	c	n	l	r	t	e
o	m	s	j	d	l	k	i	a
s	n	i	p	p	y	x	c	k
t	e	w	i	n	t	r	y	l
y	g	l	a	c	i	a	l	f

So – what have you learned about synonyms?

Focus

An **idiom** is an everyday expression used by people which **cannot be literal** (true). Idioms are used to make descriptions livelier and more interesting.

It rained cats and dogs.

I'm under the weather.

If idioms become over-used, they become **clichés**.

Check it out

1. Match the idioms from Set A to their meanings in Set B, like the first one. Write out the pairs of sentences you have made.

Set A	Set B
• I am under the weather. • He has given up the ghost. • My tomatoes grow well in the greenhouse. • She has been taken for a ride. • Let's not beat about the bush. • In for a penny, in for a pound. • People in glasshouses shouldn't throw stones. • I can't help putting his back up.	• He has died. • Let's not waste time. • Don't do to others something you don't like yourself. • I can't help annoying him. • Let's take a risk. • I don't feel well. • My tomatoes grow well in the greenhouse • She has been tricked.

2. Identify which sentence is not an idiom and explain why.

Practice

1. Explain what these idiomatic phrases really mean, for example,
over the hill means **she is no longer as good as she used to be**.

a) Past her prime.

b) Put on a brave face.

c) Over the top.

d) Par for the course.

e) A new age is dawning.

f) Go to the ends of the earth.

g) The idol of the silver screen.

2. Match the idioms above to where they were derived in the box below.

> clowns putting on make-up   exploration of the world
> score in a game of golf   religious worship   meat in a butcher's shop
> sunrise beginning a day   First World War soldiers in the trenches

3. Proverbs are idiomatic phrases, like **Too many cooks spoil the broth.**
Write five proverbs that you know
and explain what each one means.

Challenger

1. The speech in the box is written completely in idioms and clichés. Write it out
again in clear English, without any idiomatic expressions.

> Ladies and Gentlemen. I speak from the bottom of my heart. When I saw
> the bomb damage I could hardly believe my eyes. We will leave no stone
> unturned. We will go to the ends of the earth to find the villain of the
> piece. We will protect the innocent victim. There is light at the end of the
> tunnel. This government will stay by your side through thick and thin,
> until we have weathered the storm of terrorism.

So – what have you learned about idiomatic phrases and expressions?

Focus

An **adverb** is a word or phrase which **describes a verb**.
Quickly is an adverb. It describes the verb **to run**.

He runs.　　He runs quickly.

↑　　　↑　　↑
verb　　verb　adverb

Many adverbs end in **ly**, but not all.

He runs **fast**.

Adverbs help us to understand **how** things are said, and might show us something extra about the character of the person.

"I like sweets,"
she said **shyly**.

"I like sweets,"
she said **greedily**.

"I like sweets,"
she said **enviously**.

Check it out

1.　Copy these sentences in your book. Circle the adverbs and underline the verbs they qualify (refer to). The first one has been done for you.

a)　"Stop! Thief!" she <u>cried</u> (loudly.)

b)　"Do I have to do it, Mum?" she asked unenthusiastically.

c)　She told us her story, whispering quietly.

d)　The cars flew around the track quickly before getting slower.

e)　"You must work hard," the teacher told the class loudly and confidently.

f)　She cried out strongly and bravely before she was rescued.

g)　Mike spoke angrily to the man in the car but, after a time, he left smiling happily.

Practice

1. Match the verbs in Set A (all synonyms for **to say**) with the best adverb in Set B.

Set A	Set B
shout	hysterically
whisper	rudely
describe	hard
laugh	shyly
stammer	carefully
complain	softly
mumble	loudly
exclaim	excitedly
plead	hesitantly
mutter	angrily

2. Now write some sentences using the pairs of words you have matched. (You may have to change the tense of the verb.)

Challenger

1. Rewrite this passage of dialogue, punctuating it correctly. Include a suitable adverb to qualify each **said**.

> In the 1800s, teachers were paid every week in cash. I'm going to see the paymaster children said Miss Smith. Get on with some work. She returned in ten minutes.
>
> Where have you been again Miss said Fred. I've been for my wages the teacher said. Wages? said the little boy. Yes said the teacher I get paid every week. But Miss, said Fred, where do you work?

So – what have you learned about using adverbs when you write dialogue?

Focus

A **dictionary** gives you the **meaning of words**.

It can also help you to check spelling more easily because:

- it is set out in **alphabetical order**
- the entries can tell you how the word is **pronounced**
- the entries can tell you about the **derivation** of words (where words come from).

Check it out

1. Write a list of these animals. Put them in alphabetical order.

> sheep   horse   x-ray   fish   cat   rabbit   kangaroo   duck   lamb
> zebra   blackbird   goose   mouse   lion   antelope   quail

2. Answer this alphabet quiz.

a) Which letter of the alphabet is a hot drink?

b) Which letter of the alphabet is a buzzy, honey-maker?

c) Which letter of the alphabet asks a question?

d) Which letter of the alphabet makes a vegetable-bearing climbing plant?

Practice

1. If **pearl** and **pelvis** are the first and last words on a page in your dictionary, write out the 11 words from the box, in alphabetical order, which would also be found on that page.

> pedal   peep   pen   peck   peasant   pelt
> pebble   pear   pedestrian   peg   peach   peel
> peculiar   peak   pelican

2. If **invasion** and **iron** are the first and last words on a page of your dictionary, write out the ten words from the box, in alphabetical order, which would also be found on that page.

> inward   irradiate   iodine   invent   invertebrate
> Iranian   invest   invaluable   island   invitation
> invalid   iris   Irish   involved   introduce

Challenger

1. Use your dictionary to help you find out which numbers these words are associated with and write their prefixes.

> quartet   centipede   decimals   bicycle   millennium
> octave   hexagon   trio   unique   polygon

2. a) Write some other words which use the same prefixes.
   b) Write sentences using five of your new words.

So – what have you learned about using dictionaries to help you spell words correctly?

21

Unit 10 'qu' and 'tion'

Focus

A **letter string** is a group of letters which often occurs in words.
Remembering letter strings helps us to spell. For example:
ight is a common letter string in **light**, br**ight**, fr**ight**ful, alm**ight**y.

light

bright

frightful

almighty

Check it out

1. Copy the words in the table. Underline the letter strings **qu** and **tion**.

squadron	squashed	mosquitoes
attention	section	education
quite	quiet	frequently
conversation	organisation	sensation
situation	population	nations
request	liquorice	quarrel
mentioned	reception	relations
quiz	quiver	squint

Practice

1. Copy and complete these words, using the letter string **tion**.

Check your spelling in a dictionary.

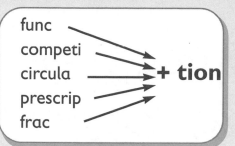

func
competi
circula   **+ tion**
prescrip
frac

perfec
exclama
informa   **+ tion**
junc
indiges

2. Use a dictionary to change the verbs in the box to nouns.

Do it like this: **to direct – the direction**

Then write the words in sentences.

create   add   subtract
prepare   compose

Challenger

1. Solve these word puzzles. All the answers contain **qu.**

a) The wife of a King.

b) A tank for fish.

c) Some old, valuable objects.

d) A large tent.

e) The feather cover for a bed.

f) You sign one to get money from a bank.

g) The only one of its kind.

h) A small animal with a bushy tail.

i) A line of people.

j) Something you ask.

2. Copy this table. Write the answers from the puzzle into the correct columns.

qu at end	**qu** in the middle	**qu** at the beginning

So – what have you learned about spelling words using the letter strings 'qu' and 'tion'?

Focus

Letters can be divided into **vowels** and **consonants**.

The **vowels** are **a, e, i, o, u**. All the other letters are **consonants**.

When you add **full** or **all** to the beginning or the end of a word, one of the **l** consonants is dropped.

I am **full** of hope.

I am hope**ful**.

Check it out

1. Write a word from List A. Match it up with two rhyming words from List B.

2. a) Which two letters do all these words have at the end?

   b) Does a vowel or a consonant always come before these final letters?

List A	List B	
hall	pull	shell
spell	pill	troll
hill	ball	grill
doll	smell	small
bull	Moll	full

Practice

1. Add the suffix **full** to each of these words. Check your answers in a dictionary.
Remember – the spelling might change!

hope
joy
play
thank

+ full

hate
cheer
tear
spoon

+ full

2. Explain what happens to the spelling of the suffix **full** when you
word-build with it.

3. Add the suffix **full** to these words.   (**beauty   skill   awe**)

Check your answers in a dictionary.

What do you notice about the spelling of the
root word which you add to the suffix **full**?

Challenger

1. Add the prefix **all** to these words. Check your answers in a dictionary.
Remember – the spelling might change!

a) ready   c) together   e) most   g) so

b) ways   d) though   f) mighty

2. Explain what happens to the spelling of the prefix **all** when
you word-build with it.

3. Write eight sentences using the new words you have made.

So – what have you learned about using 'll' when spelling?

Focus

Letters can be divided into **vowels** and **consonants**.
The **vowels** are **a, e, i, o, u**. All the other letters are **consonants**.
When you word-build by adding suffixes such as **ing** and **ed**,
sometimes the final consonant doubles.

stop   stop**ing**   stop**ed**

hop   hop**ing**

But not in words such as **hope – hoping.**

Check it out

1. a) Copy and complete the table. Use a
dictionary to check your spelling.

b) What happens to the last letter of the
root word each time?

root word	+ing	+ed
rob	robbing	robbed
shop		
beg		
hop		
pin		
sip		
sin		

Practice

1. Add **ing** to the words in the box. Check your spelling in a dictionary.

> shop   cool   win   cry   run
> get   hope   dig   fail   skip   hop
> feel   hum   come   tap

2. Copy and complete the table below with the words in the box above.

Word	No. of syllables	Last letter	Second to last letter	Third to last letter
shop	1	consonant	vowel	consonant

3. What do you notice about the words which doubled their final consonants in question 1?

Challenger

1. Write a rule to explain why some of the words in Practice question 1 doubled their final consonants when **ing** was added.

2. > **When you word-build onto a single syllable word, the final consonant doubles before adding the suffix.**

Can you find any exceptions to this rule?

3. Make more words by adding **er** and **ed**, if possible, to the words in the Practice section.

a) Explain if they follow the same rule.

b) Write sentences using five of your new words.

So – what have you learned about doubling final consonants when spelling?

Focus

Letters can be divided into **vowels** and **consonants**.
The **vowels** are **a, e, i, o, u**. All the other letters are **consonants**.

Some consonants are pronounced in a **hard** way.

The same consonants can be pronounced in a **soft** way.

The **c** in **cat** and the **g** in **get** sound **hard**.

The **c** in **pace** and the **g** in **general** sound **soft**.

Check it out

1. Copy the words in the box. Circle the **c** or **g** consonant sound.

Write if they sound **hard** or **soft** beside each word.

Do it like this: **great (hard)**

> great   cellar   disguise   cord   ceiling
> goalkeeper   cottage   manager   cupboard
> change   notice   guess   content   ranger
> gift   centre   damage   rice   coal

Practice

1. Copy the vowel table below. Put the **c** words in the correct columns, according to which vowel comes after the **c**.

a	e	i	o	u
card				

cat	custard	record
circle	France	cabbage
cut	pencil	cement
city	cell	content
card	come	cup

What do you notice about the sounds of the **c** words in each column?

2. Copy the vowel table below. Put the **g** words in the correct columns, according to which vowel comes after the **g**.

a	e	i	o	u
gasp				

gasp	guitar	gin
gem	gape	gold
gulf	gone	damage
gate	general	god
giraffe	tongue	giant

What do you notice about the sounds of the **g** words in each column?

Challenger

1. Complete these rules about when **c** and **g** are hard or soft:

a) The letter **c** is pronounced soft if it appears before ...

b) Before other vowels **c** is ...

c) The letter **g** is pronounced soft if it appears before ...

d) Before other vowels **g** is ...

2. Use a dictionary to find three more examples and three exceptions to question 1. Use five of your words in sentences.

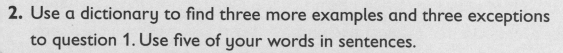

So – what have you learned about hard and soft consonants and spelling patterns?

Focus

A **letter string** is a group of letters which often occur in words. Remembering letter strings can help us to spell, but sometimes the same letter string, for example, **ough**, can be pronounced in many different ways — **tough, although, plough, thought.**

Check it out

1. Copy the table.

a) Underline the common letter string in each word in each row.

b) Circle the word with a different pronunciation in each row. The first one has been done for you.

br<u>ow</u>n	fr<u>ow</u>n	gr<u>ow</u>l	show
rough	tough	plough	enough
moon	blood	tool	boot
could	flour	sour	hourly
pain	Spain	raining	said
heating	bear	treatment	seat
floating	coat	roar	moat

Practice

1. These words have common letter strings but are pronounced differently and mean something different. Use a dictionary to write sentences showing their different meanings. The clues in the first one will start you off.

a) bow (firing arrows)   bow (bend down low)
b) sow   sow
c) row   row
d) wind   wind
e) read   read

Challenger

1. Copy and complete the table below.

   Choose the **ough** words from the box which are pronounced the same way as these five words. Write them beneath the same-sounding words.

fought	rough	dough	plough	cough

cough	bought	through	although	tough	thought
ought	thorough	enough	trough	bough	nought
	drought	although	though	hiccough	

   Which words do not fit into any of the columns?

2. Write five sentences using one **ough** word from each column.

So – what have you learned about common letter strings which have different pronunciations?

Homophones

Focus

The **poor** dog has hurt its **paw**. **Pour** it a drink of water.

These three words sound the same but have different meanings and are spelled differently. They are **homophones.**	The phonemes sound the same, even though they are made from different letters.

Check it out

1. Copy these sentences in your book. Underline the homophones. The first one has been done for you.

a) He <u>ate</u> dinner every day at <u>eight</u>.

b) The saw cut his hand and his fingers felt sore all week.

c) In the film, the criminals tried to steal the money from the steel strong room.

d) A hare is like a rabbit but with shorter hair.

e) Lewis Carroll wrote a tale about a mouse with a very long tail.

f) The naval commander bought a new sail for the ship at the dockyard sale.

g) She drew a flower shape in the spilled flour in the kitchen.

h) What do you call a bear in the shower? A bare bear!

2. Use a dictionary to find out what each homophone means.

Practice

1. Match up the pairs of homophones from the box. Write them out.

> fur course stair fir allowed read write
> stare reed coarse aloud right

2. Copy the sentences. Choose the correct homophone from the box to fill each gap.

a) Many people think it is cruel to make _____ coats.

b) To _____ at someone is considered rude.

c) He was not _____ to go to the concert.

d) This is not the _____ answer.

e) I learned to _____ books when I was five.

f) The material of the jacket felt very _____.

3. Write six sentences using the remaining homophones in the box.

Challenger

1. Copy the chart. Match the homophones in the first two sets. Find the third homophone and write them in.
Use a dictionary to help.

2. Write a sentence to use each new word you have found.

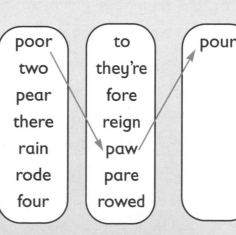

poor	to	pour
two	they're	
pear	fore	
there	reign	
rain	paw	
rode	pare	
four	rowed	

So – what have you learned about using homophones?

Focus

A **pronoun** is a word we use **instead of a noun**. There are various kinds of pronouns, some of which are **possessive pronouns**.
Possessive pronouns are: **mine**, **his**, **hers**, **its**, **ours**, **yours**, **theirs**, **whose**.

Is it yours or theirs?

Possessive pronouns can be confused with similar sounding words but they **never** take an apostrophe. **The dog has hurt its tail** is very different from **It's a very long tail.**

No, it's mine.

Check it out

1. Write out **only** the sentences which contain possessive pronouns and underline these words. The first one has been done for you.

a) <u>Yours</u> are all on the shelf over there. <u>Mine</u> are here.

b) It's a very hot day so I'm going to play in the pool.

c) Who's coming to the beach this afternoon with them?

d) The dog was chasing its tail, round and round. His tongue was hanging out.

e) That car is red, hers is blue and his is black.

f) Whose house is this? Is it yours or theirs?

g) Their present is exactly like my mother's gift, but they're not embarrassed.

h) I like her garden with its own pond. Ours is very similar.

Practice

1. Rewrite these sentences in your book, choosing the correct words from the choices given.

a) Is that (there, their, mine) skateboard or does it belong to you?

b) That skateboard is (theirs, they're, there's) and does not belong to you.

c) Are (yours, your, who's) CD-Roms compatible with my computer?

d) Don't tell me they are if (you're, your, its) not sure.

e) Which of these CD-Roms are (my, your, yours)?

f) (You're, Your, You) car is much bigger than (our, ours).

g) (Theirs, whose, there's) is a Rolls Royce and ours is only a Mini.

h) Our car was cheap. (Your, You're, Yours) must have been expensive.

i) (Who, Who's, Whose) is that signed season ticket on the shelf?

j) The team signatures are (her, him, hers).

k) (It's, Its, It) priceless!

2. List all the possessive pronouns that you've used in the sentences above.

Challenger

1. Write each of these words in sentences of your own.
   Underline the words which are possessive pronouns.
   Circle the words which are contractions.

a) mine	e) it's	i) you're	m) they're
b) his	f) ours	j) theirs	n) whose
c) hers	g) yours	k) their	o) who's
d) its	h) your	l) there	p) there's

So – what have you learned about the correct use and spelling of possessive pronouns?

Focus

An **antonym** is a word meaning the **opposite**. For example, the antonym for **hot** is **cold.** Some words have more than one opposite, for example, the opposite of **big** can be **small** or **tiny**, etc. Other words have no opposite, for example, colours such as **green**.

Check it out

1. Copy the examples. Circle the antonym of the key word.

2. Use a dictionary or thesaurus to check your answers.

Key word	Antonym
dirty	muddy unclean filthy (clean)
fall	hill rise drop trip
small	petite tiny huge piece
polite	manners rough rude nice
weak	feeble effort strong low
gentle	safe mild kind rough
large	big small grand enormous
rough	dark light dirty smooth

Practice

1. One way to make words opposite is to use negative prefixes. Add the correct prefixes to the words to make twelve antonyms. Write out the twelve words you have made. Check in a dictionary.

Prefixes	Words	
in	continue	patient
il	experience	pleasant
im	logical	literate
ir	regular	happy
un	agree	mature
dis	convenient	reversible

2. Make five antonyms of your own using new words and the prefixes. Write sentences using them.

Challenger

1. Use a dictionary and a thesaurus.

a) Find antonyms for as many of the words in the table below as possible.
b) Which words do not have an antonym?
c) Use eight antonyms in sentences.

Nouns	Adjectives	Adverbs	Verbs
cushion	rough	expensively	to weaken
echo	blue	obediently	to dribble
childhood	empty	thoughtfully	to drown
elbow	double	fast	to arrive
price	triangular	anxiously	to admit

So – what have you learned about antonyms?

Focus

Onomatopoeic words actually make the noise they are describing.
For example: The bacon **crackles** in the pan; Our balloons **popped**
near the fire; "**Woof, woof**," the dog barked.

Woof, woof

Check it out

1. Copy these sets of words. Underline the onomatopoeic word in each line.
   The first one has been done for you.

a) grassy   gravel   <u>growl</u>   grow

b) through   thud   them   Thursday

c) hummed   humid   humble   human

d) chips   choppy   character   chirp

e) wizard   whizzed   which   whenever

f) screech   scrabble   scrawny   shrimp

g) pin   push   penguin   ping

2. Explain why you chose the word in each example.

Practice

1. These onomatopoeic words describe noises made by animals.

Match the animals to their sounds and write them in pairs.

Sound		
yap	coo	hoot
caw	hiss	croak
buzz	moo	howl
bleat	cheep	purr
cluck	bray	quack
neigh	gobble	grunt

Animal		
pigs	snakes	owls
chicks	ducks	cows
frogs	lambs	cats
turkeys	bees	crows
chickens	pigeons	donkeys
wolves	horses	puppies

2. Put five of the word pairs into sentences. You may need to change the tense of the verb. For example, **the pigs <u>grunted</u> happily in the farmyard**.

Challenger

1. Match the onomatopoeic words to their actions.

Write a sentence using each of the words as verbs.

Onomatopoeic word	Action being described
crack	bottles being moved in crates
whir	sausages exploding in a pan
clatter	windows breaking
rattle	helicopter blades rotating
splash	jumping on ice in a puddle
pop	falling into a swimming pool
crash	plates being washed

2. Make up some of your own onomatopoeic words to describe a washing machine. For example, it could be **splishy** and could **splitter** against the glass.

So – what have you learned about onomatopoeic words?

Focus

A **metaphor** is really a comparison of two things. The writer does not say one thing **is like** something else, but says **it is** something else.

> Tom is a silly boy.
> He is an ass.

Remember: metaphorical expressions cannot be literal (be true).

Idioms and **proverbs** make use of **metaphorical expressions**.

> He let the cat out of the bag.

Check it out

1. Match the two parts of the proverbs and write them out in sentences.

When the cat's away	and eat it.
Better late	by its cover.
Never judge a book	the mice will play.
You can't have your cake	make light work.
Those who live in glass houses	than never.
Many hands	shouldn't throw stones.

Now find two more proverbs to add to your list.

2. Explain what each proverb actually means.

Practice

1. Copy and complete the table below.

Write the expressions below in the correct columns.

Metaphorical expression	Literal expression

- he was a lion in battle
- filled their hearts with fear
- a lion in a cage
- get to the bottom of the affair
- reared its ugly head
- swam in the sea
- the insect was trapped in the web
- one eye fixed on the future
- an ear to the ground
- kicked the bucket
- he scratched his ear
- lost the thread of the argument
- she filled a bucket with water
- one eye was closed
- he was all at sea
- a web of lies
- his back to the wall
- buried his head in the sand
- pulled the thread through with a needle

Challenger

1. Metaphorical expressions are sometimes confusing.

Rewrite the sentences in straightforward English.

a) Sheila seemed to have her head in the clouds, but her feet were planted on the ground.

b) He remained sitting on the fence during the argument.

c) Ranjit needed to finish his homework so he put his shoulder to the wheel and took the bit between his teeth.

d) She sailed into action, bulldozing her way through the team.

2. Explain the derivation of these everyday expressions. Do it like this:

to <u>have your head in the clouds</u> means to be dreaming.

So – what have you learned about metaphorical expressions?

Focus

It is possible to build up **longer** words from **smaller** words, or parts of words. If you know the **spelling** and the **meaning** of one word, it can help you to spell a variety of words.

If you can spell **press**, then you can spell…

…**depress, express, impress, suppress, repress, Empress** just by adding **prefixes**.

If you can spell **sign**, then you can spell…

…**signal, significant, signature** just by adding **suffixes**.

It can help to know the **derivation** of words, for example, that **dis** or **mis** at the beginning of a word makes it mean the opposite:
approve – disapprove, understand – misunderstand

Check it out

1. Copy these examples. Underline the word or part of the word which appears in each set. The first one has been done for you.

a) <u>play</u>ground, <u>play</u>group, <u>play</u>thing

b) telephone, telescopic, television

c) xylophone, microphone, headphone

d) advent, invention, preventing

e) reigning, sovereign, foreign

f) disgraceful, graced, gracious

g) appearance, disappear, appeared

h) government, governer, govern

2. Use your dictionary to find out what the words all mean. Use one from each set to write a sentence.

Practice

1. You can build compound words from known words (words made up of one or more word).

   play + ground   play + house   play + thing

   List at least two compound words built from each of these words.

   a) silver +   d) mother +   g) ear +   j) red +

   b) heir +   e) stock +   h) sun +   k) snow +

   c) some +   f) open +   i) foot +   l) counter +

2. Use your dictionary to find out what these new words mean and to check your spelling.

Challenger

1. Add prefixes and suffixes to each of the known words to make as many words from it as possible.

   Do it like this: **appear** could make: **appears, reappear, appearance, disappear, disappearing**, and so on.

Known words	Prefixes	Suffixes
approve	dis	ing
continue	un	ed
assume	in	ance
crease	de	al
direct	mis	s
part	im	ure
place	re	ment
fresh		

So – what have you learned about word-building from known words?

Focus

A **polysyllabic** word is a word with **more than one syllable.**

Syllable has three syllables **syl   la   ble**
                                     1   2   3

Sometimes, vowels in these words are not always **stressed**, or pronounced, and so they become difficult to spell.

What a lovely **ma/gic po/tion**!

Check it out

1. Join up the syllables in each word sum and write the word. Write the number of syllables in brackets after the word.

Do it like this: **com + put + er = computer (3)**

a) some + thing =

b) sta + tion + ary =

c) com + pa + ny =

d) Sa + tur + day =

e) tem + per + at + ture =

f) im + por + tant =

g) thes + au + rus =

Practice

1. Copy these words and write in the missing vowels.

a) t_rr_f_c

b) b_ _ _ _t_f_l

c) c_mp_ng

d) _nt_r_st_ng

e) d_ff_r_nt

f) p_ _ _s_n_ _s

g) st_t_ _n_ry

h) p_rt_bl_

i) c_rp_t

j) fr_ _d_m

k) _xtr_ _ _rd_n_ry

l) tr_ _ _n_r

Now break up the words into syllables, using /. Do it like this: **hol/ly**
Finally, circle the vowels which you think are likely to get left out when
spelling the word, because they are unstressed. Do it like this: **diff(e)rent**

Challenger

1. Copy and complete the table below, using the words in
the box. This will show how the structure and derivation
of words can help you to spell them.

signature
celebration
temperature
independence
description

Word root	Prefix	Suffix
sign	–	ature

2. Write some mnemonics to help you spell these words. Use the
clues in brackets. For example, there's a **rat** in **separate**.

a) temperature (temper)

b) company (pan)

c) practice (ice)

d) interesting (rest)

So – what have you learned about using
punctuation effectively for meaning?

Focus

Sometimes, when you word-build onto a word ending in **e**, you may not be sure whether to **drop** the final e or **keep** it.

Care...

Careful?

Caring?

Lovely?

Love...

Loving?

By working through the exercises in this Unit, you should be able to come to some conclusions about dropping or keeping the **e**.

Check it out

1. Copy and complete the table.
   Add the suffix **ing** to these words.
   Check your words in a dictionary.

2. Explain what you notice has happened
   to the spelling of these words when
   the suffix **ing** is added.

root word	+ ing
write	
care	
ride	
hope	
love	
come	
believe	
delete	

Practice

1. Add the suffix **full** to these words. Write the new word.
Check your answers in a dictionary.

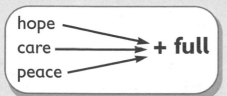

hope
care → + full
peace

2. Add the suffix **ly** to these words. Write the new word.
Check your answers in a dictionary.

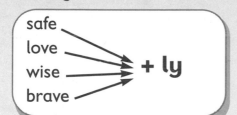

safe
love
wise → + ly
brave

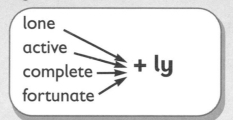

lone
active
complete → + ly
fortunate

Challenger

1. Complete these rules to explain what you have discovered in the three
exercises about adding suffixes to words ending in **e**.

a) When you add the suffix **ing** to a word ending in e ...

b) When you add the suffix **full** to words ending in e ...

c) When you add the suffix **ly** to words ending in e ...

2. Find three more examples to illustrate each of these three rules.

3. Find some exceptions to the rules, for example, what happens when you word-
build using the suffixes **ing**, **full** and **ly** with:

> **tie   lie   die   probable   possible   terrible   single   simple**

**So – what have you learned about word-building
onto words ending in an 'e'?**

Focus

Sometimes, when you word-build on to a word ending in **y**, you may not be sure whether to **change** the final **y** or **keep** it.

By working through the exercises in this Unit, you should be able to come to some conclusions about changing or keeping the **y**.

Check it out

1. Write out the nouns below in the plural. All the answers end in **s**, but check your spellings in a dictionary.

a) one monkey, two <u>monkeys</u>   f) one valley, two _____

b) one lady, two _____   g) one ruby, two _____

c) one berry, two _____   h) one key, two _____

d) one country, two _____   i) one toy, two _____

e) one copy, two _____   j) one baby, two _____

2. Write a rule to explain how you make nouns ending in **y** into the plural.

Practice

1. Copy and complete the table using the verbs in the box. Check your spellings in a dictionary.

Verbs

carry annoy reply stay play worry
dry delay marry destroy enjoy copy

Verb	Last letter	Second to last letter	Add **ed** to verb	Add **s** to verb
carry	consonant	consonant	carried	carries

2. Write a rule to explain whether or not the spelling of the verb changes when you add **ed** or **s**.

Challenger

1. a) Add **ing** to these verbs:

apply study copy bury reply cry

Explain what happens.

b) Add **ly** to these adjectives:

happy easy lazy beauty heavy pretty steady

Explain what happens. Check your spellings in a dictionary.

2. Add **ing**, **d** and **s** to: **die**, **tie** and **lie**. Check your spellings in a dictionary. What happens to the spellings in each case?

So – what have you learned about word-building on to words ending in 'y'?

Focus

Sometimes, when you spell a word (usually containing the **ee** phoneme), you may not be sure whether to put **ei** or **ie**.

Is it **i** before **e**?

Receive?

Relief?

By working through the exercises in this Unit, you should be able to come to some conclusions about which to use, **ei** or **ie**.

Check it out

1. One word in each pair of words below is spelled incorrectly. Use your dictionary to check the spelling of each one.
   Write each pair of words, spelled correctly.

a) chief, freind

b) handkercheif, ceiling

c) theif, field

d) percieve, Keith

e) seige, priest

f) hieght, deceiver

g) queit, seize

Practice

1. Put **ie** or **ei** into the following words. Use a dictionary to help.
Write out the correct words.

bel__ __ve	y__ __ ld	gr__ __ f	rec__ __ve	br__ __f
ach__ __ve	dec__ __ve	gr__ __ving	conc__ __ve	p__ __ce
sh__ __ld	rel__ __f	p__ __r	dec__ __t	s__ __ge
rec__ __pt	conc__ __t	n__ __c e		

2. Copy and complete the table below using the
words you have just completed in question 1.

Words containing **ie**	Letter before **ie**
piece	p

Words containing **ei**	Letter before **ei**

What sound does the **ie** or **ei** make in all these words?

Challenger

1. Copy and complete the rule below. Include the sound that all the words have
in common and look closely at the letter which comes before **ie/ei**.

> Put i before ___ except after ___ when it makes the sound **ee**.

Now write four more words into your table which prove your rule.

2. Use your dictionary to find five exceptions to the rule, like **seize**.

3. Write some sentences using five of the words in your table.

So – what have you learned about spelling words with 'ie' or 'ei'?

Focus

The spelling of words can alter when you **transform** (change) a word into a different **verb tense**. For example, **I see, I am seeing, I saw** or into a different **part of speech**, for example, from a **noun to an adjective** as in **friend** to **friendly**.

I see.   I am seeing.   I saw.

Check it out

1. Copy the table. Match each verb with its form in different tenses. Describe the changes in spelling.

Verb	Present tense	Past tense	How has the spelling changed?
come	beginning	jumped	
jump	hoping	ran	
run	hopping	swam	
begin	coming	began	
hope	swimming	hopped	
hop	jumping	hoped	
swim	running	came	

Practice

1. Make nouns from these verbs by adding **ion**.
   Check your spellings in a dictionary.

   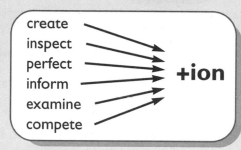

   create
   inspect
   perfect
   inform   **+ion**
   examine
   compete

2. Make verbs from the following nouns.

   knee becomes **to kneel**   **spark** becomes

   song becomes   **bright** becomes

   threat becomes   **paint** becomes

   Check your spellings in a dictionary.

3. Write some sentences using five of the new words you have made in this section.

Challenger

1. Add a suffix from the box to change these words into different
   parts of speech. Use your dictionary to check your spellings.

   ness   th
      ship

   hard (adjective to noun)   **ten** (noun to adjective)

   friend (common noun to abstract noun)   **warm** (adjective to noun)

   member (noun to abstract noun)   **nine** (noun to adjective)

2. Copy and complete the tables. Add a suffix from the box
   to change these adjectives into nouns. Use your dictionary.

   ty   y   th
   ness   ity   ce

Adjective	Noun	Adjective	Noun	Adjective	Noun
good		beautiful		long	
loyal		lonely		innocent	
violent		strong		friendly	
vain		young		sincere	

**So – what have you learned about how spelling
changes when transforming words?**

Focus

A **prefix** is a group of letters we add to the **beginning** of a word, or to a word root, to **change its meaning**, for example, **pre + fix.**

There are a group of prefixes which we call **negative prefixes** because they make the original word into an **antonym** (its opposite).

For example, **happy – un + happy**   **appear – dis + appear**

pre fix   dis appear   un happy

Check it out

1. Add **un** to these words to make them into antonyms (opposites).
   Write out the new word and check your spelling in a dictionary.

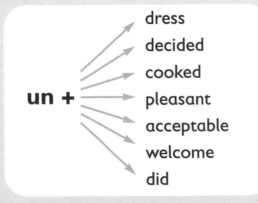

un +
- dress
- decided
- cooked
- pleasant
- acceptable
- welcome
- did

2. Say whether or not the prefix or the root word changes its spelling in each word.

Practice

1. Choose negative prefixes from the box to make each of these words into antonyms. Write out your new words.

a) justice   f) sufficient

b) polite   g) literate

c) approve   h) colour

d) behave   i) trust

e) possible   j) honest

| in | dis | mis | im | il |

2. Find some more examples of antonyms containing these negative prefixes.

Say whether or not the prefix or the root word changes its spelling in each case.

Challenger

1. Copy and complete the table below.
Use a dictionary and a thesaurus to help.

Word	Antonym using negative prefix
experience	
logical	
mature	
regular	
possible	
complete	
legal	
reversible	

So – what have you learned about the spelling and meaning of negative prefixes?

Focus

When we compare adjectives, we call them **comparative adjectives**.

This cat is **big**.

My cat is **bigger**.

Out of all the cats, mine is the **biggest**.

When adjectives are longer, we use the words **more** and **most**.

This skateboard is **beautiful**.

Mine is **more beautiful**.

Hers is the **most beautiful**.

Check it out

1. Copy and complete the table. Check your answers in a dictionary. Describe any changes in spelling that take place when the words are transformed.

Adjective	Add **er**	Add **est**	Changes in spelling
old	older		
strong			
warm			
short			
hot			
lucky			
thin			
strange			
straight			

Practice

1. a) Write some sentences using the words below. Do it like this:

My cat is big. Yours is bigger. Hers is the biggest.

Check your spellings in a dictionary.

> big   late   safe   early   noisy
>
> sad   easy   red   wet   wise

b) Explain the changes in spelling which occur when the words are transformed (for example, the final consonant **g** doubles in **bigger** and **biggest**). Give reasons for the changes. (For example, when you word-build on to a single syllable word, if a vowel comes before the last consonant, the last letter doubles.)

Challenger

1. Write the two comparative forms for each of these adjectives.

a) beautiful
b) merciful
c) dangerous
d) deserving
e) pleasant
f) handsome

2. Write the comparative forms of these tricky adjectives.

> bad   good   far   little   many

So – what have you learned about using making and spelling comparatives?

Unit 28 Other languages

Focus

The English language is always **changing**. Each time England was invaded, many hundreds of years ago – by the Romans, by the Vikings, by the French – a new language was introduced and words from these new languages were added to our own.

New words continued to be added in the nineteenth century through our connection with India and places beyond Europe. Words are still being **added** today, many from America, and through films and music.

Norse: **skirt**.

Latin: **index**.

French: **café**.

Check it out

1. Copy these words to do with food and eating. Use a dictionary to write what they mean and from which country they are derived.

a) dessert   c) café   e) menu
b) buffet   d) chef   f) hors d'oeuvre

2. Match the foods in List A with the country from which they are derived. Write the pairs of words in sentences Use your dictionary to help.

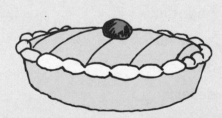

List A	Country
pizza	Africa
fries	Mexico
samosa	Italy
cola	USA
chocolate	India

Practice

1. Use your dictionary, and other reference sources, to sort the words and abbreviations below into their country of origin. Draw a table with these headings: Arabic, Italian, French, Latin and American. Complete the table using these words:

mosque	supermarket	piano	pm	fiancée
caravan	gangster	soprano	am	au pair
sherbert	teenager	opera	AD	ballet
alcohol	detergent	dome	per annum	garage
mattress	cookie	spaghetti	centurion	lieutenant

2. Find another word to write in each set.

Challenger

1. Find out in which countries these sports originated.

a) hockey   c) skiing   e) judo
b) tobogganing   d) baseball   f) karate

2. Find out from which countries these words have been borrowed.

a) buoy   d) lantern   g) moccasin   j) pyjamas
b) cot   e) tomato   h) tobacco   k) yacht
c) khaki   f) bungalow   i) waltz   l) yoghurt

3. Look up and write the meanings of any words above you do not know.

Now use five of the words in sentences to show you understand what they mean.

So – what have you learned about words from other languages?

Focus

Dictionaries can help you to find out what abbreviations mean:

- **abbreviations** are shortened forms of words or phrases, e.g. **RSVP** on the bottom of an invitation is a request for you to reply

- **dictionaries** can also tell you how these abbreviations were derived, e.g. **RSVP** is the shortened version of the French expression, **R**espondez-vous **s**'il **v**ous **p**lait

- **acronyms** are abbreviations, but are whole words formed from the first letters of other words, e.g. **RADAR** comes from **RA**dio **D**etection **A**nd **R**anging.

Respondez-vous **s**'il **v**ous **p**lait.

R A D A R

RAdio **D**etection **A**nd **R**anging

Check it out

1. Write these abbreviations in full.

a) mph   c) BC   e) BBC   g) USA

b) Anon   d) AD   f) SOS   h) RSPCA

2. Explain the derivation and meaning of these abbreviations.

a) o'clock   b) Hallowe'en   c) pm   d) am

Practice

1. Copy this note, writing all the abbreviations in full.

> Mr and Mrs Nagenda live in Peace St, close to the Elland Rd
> football stadium. It is two km from Trafalgar Sq and opposite the
> pk. They will meet us on Sat morn or Sun aft.
>
> Mr and Mrs Nagenda own their own business – Nagenda and
> Co Ltd I am in charge of the art dept.
>
> See you soon.
>
> Ray
>
> PS Forgot to ask you to bring some food, etc.
>
> Please call if there is a problem. The tel. no. is: 0612 9348.

2. What do you notice about the punctuation in the abbreviations?
Find the derivation of Mr, Mrs, etc. and PS in the dictionary.

3. Find out the origin of these acronyms: **ROM**, **NAAFI**, **WRENS**.

Challenger

1. Copy and complete the table.

Use your dictionary and other reference sources to complete it.

Shortened word	Original longer word(s)	Parts missed out
bus	omnibus	omni
phone		
mac		
plane		
pram		
fridge		
photo		
amps		
piano		
perm		

So – what have you learned about using dictionaries
to find out about and spell abbreviations?

Focus

Longer words can be broken down into smaller parts called **syllables**.
Bad has one syllable. **Bad/min/ton** has three syllables.

- Each **syllable** must contain at least one vowel sound.
- **Syllables** do not have to make whole words by themselves.
- Breaking words into **syllables** is a good way to see how words are built up.
- You can also construct new words from separate **syllables**.

Compound words are words made up of complete other words.

any + one = anyone   black + berry = blackberry

Check it out

1. Write out the words which are the answers to these syllable sums,
then write the number of syllables in each word in brackets.
The first one has been done for you.

a) birth + day = <u>birthday (2)</u>

b) chil + dren = _____

c) swim + ming = _____

d) veg + et + able = _____

e) fol + low + ing= _____

f) an + im + als = _____

g) bi + cy + cle = _____

h) im + por + tant = _____

i) bal + loon = _____

j) com + for + ta + ble = _____

k) dan + ger + ous = _____

l) ne + ces + sary = _____

Practice

1. a) Copy and complete the table. Make some three-syllable
   words, like the example.

1st syllable	2nd syllable	3rd syllable	Complete word	Similar Words
sig	ledge	ine	signature	sign
know	nat	ion		
med	pic	ic		
sus	ic	ite		
rel	tall	ient		
me	at	ive		
de	co	ure		
dis	fin	able		
eff	ic	ver		

b) Look for the similar spellings in the box, and
write them in the last column. Write them beside
the most similar word.

Similar words

sign, know, medical,
suspect, relate, metal,
finite, cover, effect.

Challenger

1. Make as many
   compound words as
   you can from these
   single-syllable words.

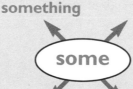
something

some

head

play

hand

school

So – what have you learned about building up spelling by syllables?

Range of Books Available

Year 3 Sentence	Year 4 Sentence	Year 5 Sentence	Year 6 Sentence
Year 3 Word	Year 4 Word	Year 5 Word	Year 6 Word

Literacy Differentiation Word Level Year 5

First published 1999
Reprinted 1999, 2000, 2001

Letts Educational,
414 Chiswick High Road, London W4 5TF
Tel: 020 8996 3333   Fax: 020 8742 8390

Text © Louis Fidge and Ray Barker

Illustrations © Phil Burrows, Richard Duszsczak, Simon Girling & Associates (Liz Sawyer), David Lock, Tim Oliver, John Plumb, Sylvie Poggio Artists Agency (Simon Jacobs) and Ken Vail Graphic Design (Liz Bryan)

Designed by Ken Vail Graphic Design, Cambridge

British Library Cataloguing-in-Publication Data
A CIP record for this book is available from the British Library

ISBN: 1 84085 235 6

Printed in the UK by Ashford Colour Press

Every effort has been made to trace copyright holders and to obtain their permission for the use of copyright material. The authors and publishers would gladly receive information enabling them to rectify an error or omission in subsequent editions.

Letts Educational Ltd, a division of Granada Learning Ltd. Part of the Granada Media Group.